CENTRAL LIBRARY

D1034656

GROWING UP WITH MUSIC

SONGS OF NORWAY AND DENMARK

by

Beatrice Perham Krone

and

Ruth Vivian Ostlund

Illustrated by

George Shealy

Price 50c

$1.00

Printed in U. S. A.

Published by

NEIL A. KJOS MUSIC CO.

CHICAGO

CONTENTS

June 15, 1843 September 4, 1907

Grieg

INTRODUCTION

Vikings is the name given to the people who lived long ago in what is now the Scandinavian peninsula. If you will look at the map, you will see there is a great deal of sea coast on this peninsula. It was natural, then, that the Vikings should take to the sea for their livelihood and their pleasure.

The word *Viking* comes from *vik*, which means "harbor." Thus the Vikings were people of the harbor because their stout wooden ships swarmed the harbors.

The Vikings were brave, strong, daring, and fearless, and more at home on the water than they were on land. You probably have seen pictures of their ships. They were made of wood, and sometimes were eighty feet long. They had carved prows, many oars, masts and sails. In these ships the Vikings dared to go over the seas to many parts of the world. They even went to Greenland and North America.

We cannot know all there is to know about these Vikings without studying their old songs, for like many ancient peoples, they used music as a record of many of their adventures, their hopes, and their beliefs.

NORWEGIAN MUSIC

The Vikings in Iceland

The Vikings discovered Iceland about 860 A. D. After that discovery, more and more of the Norwegians sailed to Iceland to make it their home, because political troubles had made them unhappy in their own country.

Winters in Iceland are very long and cold, and the people turned to story-telling for entertainment. These stories were often about their own experiences, or the experiences of some member of their family. Like all story tellers, they wanted to impress their audiences. So they mixed in some very fanciful and imaginative parts along with the facts, and the result was an heroic tale, called a "saga." Some of the songs in this book are based upon these sagas. They have been told and sung by father to son and in that way preserved for hundreds of years.

This song, called *Iceland,* tells the story of the early Norwegian forefathers who emigrated to Iceland, and made that island their home. Iceland has been called the birthplace of the saga. *Iceland,* by the way, means *island,* not a land of ice!

Iceland

Text adapted from translation by R. O.

Norse Folk Song
Arr. by B. P. K.

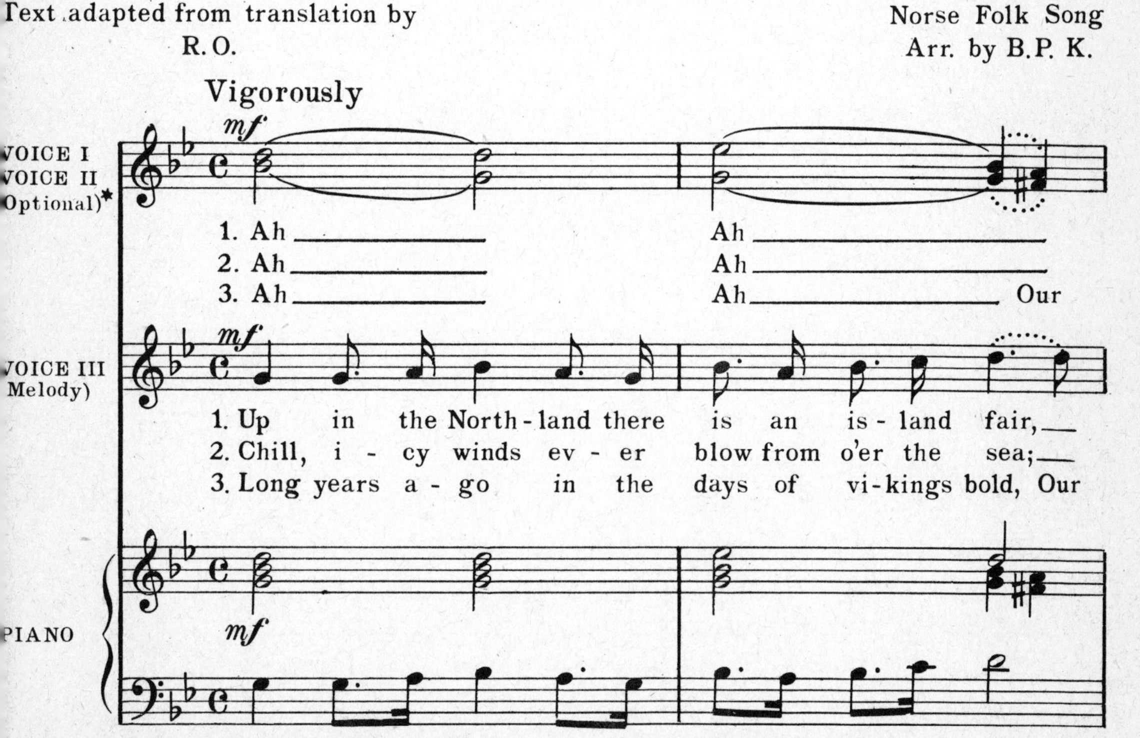

* Although most of the songs in this book have been arranged for two or three voices, they may all be sung as unison songs if desired.

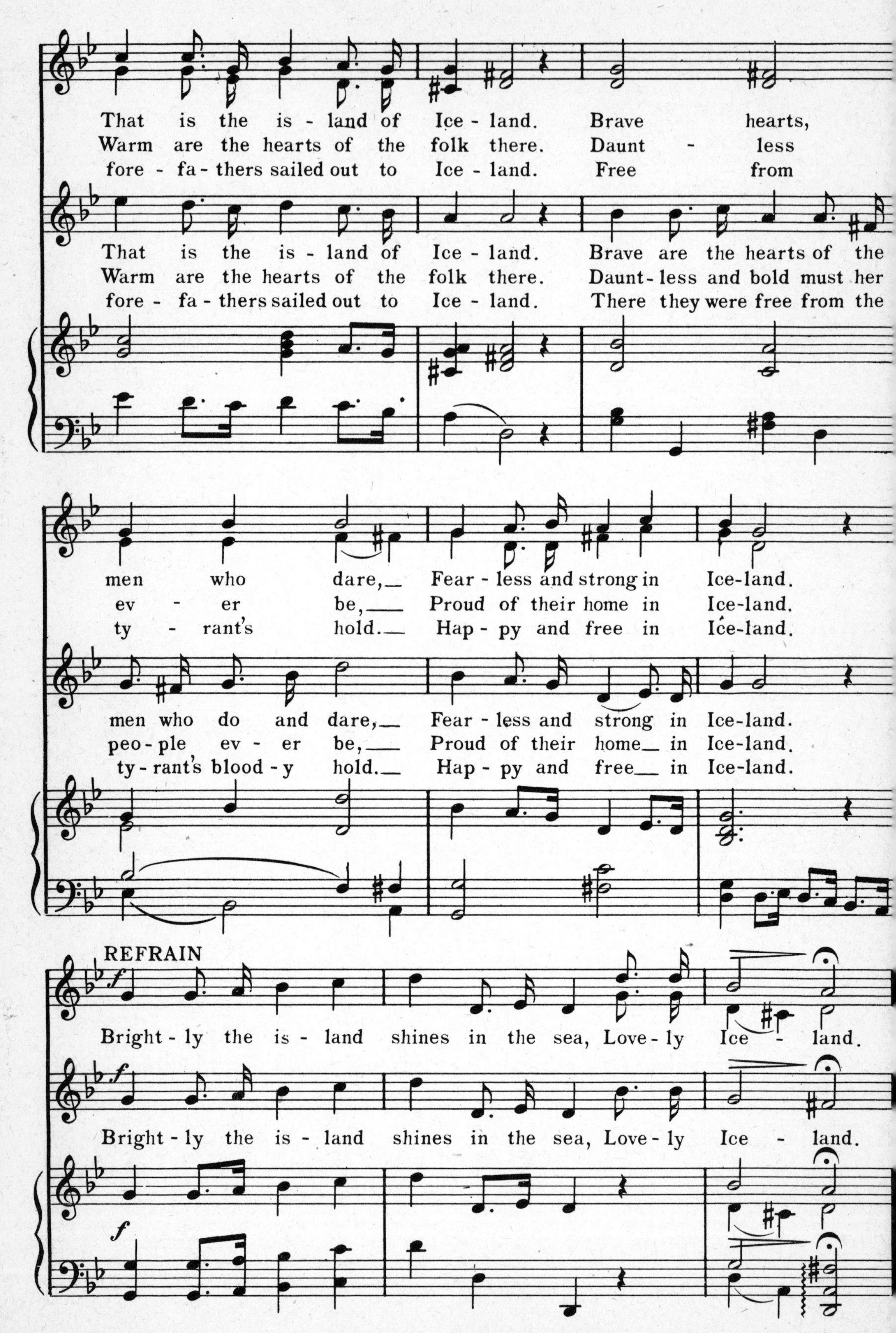
That is the is - land of Ice - land. Brave hearts,
Warm are the hearts of the folk there. Daunt - less
fore - fa - thers sailed out to Ice - land. Free from
That is the is - land of Ice - land. Brave are the hearts of the
Warm are the hearts of the folk there. Daunt - less and bold must her
fore - fa - thers sailed out to Ice - land. There they were free from the
men who dare, Fear - less and strong in Ice-land.
ev - er be, Proud of their home in Ice-land.
ty - rant's hold. Hap - py and free in Ice-land.
men who do and dare, Fear - less and strong in Ice-land.
peo - ple ev - er be, Proud of their home in Ice-land.
ty - rant's blood - y hold. Hap - py and free in Ice-land.
REFRAIN
Bright - ly the is - land shines in the sea, Love - ly Ice - land.
Bright - ly the is - land shines in the sea, Love - ly Ice - land.

THE SAGA OF FRIDTHJOF* AND INGEBORG

Long, long ago there lived a princess whose name was Ingeborg. She had two brothers, Helge and Halfdan. Their father was Bele, King of Sweden. The three children grew up with Fridthjof, the son of Thorstein, who was a wealthy landowner, and a life-long friend of King Bele's. The two fathers died, and Helge, the older of the two brothers, became guardian of Ingeborg.

At his father's death Fridthjof received not only Framness, the home of his ancestors, but three more gifts which he greatly prized, a magic sword, a wonderful arm-bracelet, and a magic ship, named Ellide.†

The spring after his father's death Fridthjof embarked in Ellide and sailed to Ingeborg's palace to ask for her hand in marriage. But Helge, instead of giving him Ingeborg, insulted Fridthjof by saying that his place was with the servants, since he was not of noble birth.

Far from the land of Ingeborg was the country of King Ring, an old but a very wise and kindly king. He sent messengers with gifts to Helge to ask for the hand of Ingeborg. Helge consulted the oracle, who advised him that Ingeborg should *not* marry King Ring. So Ingeborg was placed in safe keeping in the temple of Balder the Beautiful, who was one of the Norsemen's favorite gods.

Although he should not have done so, Fridthjof visited Ingeborg in Balder's temple to urge her to go with him in Ellide to Framness, his home. But Ingeborg would not go, even though she really loved Fridthjof.

Then Fridthjof set off on a journey, and on his return he stopped to see his old home, Framness. What was his grief to find it in smoking ruins, burned to the ground. Then he learned that a fierce battle had taken place between Helge and King Ring. Ring, the victor, had taken Ingeborg as his prize. Helge had set fire to Framness as he left.

Fridthjof was broken hearted, and for a long time he sailed with his faithful followers over the sea as a Viking.

*Pronounced Frit-chof. †Pronounced El-lé-de.

When Fridthjof first set out with his Viking crew, they all agreed upon certain rules which would regulate their conduct while they were out on raiding expeditions. These rules were, in effect:

Always sleep with shield and sword at side.

Only the sky shall be our coverlet.

Merchant ships shall be unmolested, but shall pay tribute to us.

If a fighting ship draw near, board it at once, for a fight is the joy of the brave.

He who shows signs of fear is dismissed from our band, and no pleading can save him from his cowardice.

When victory is won, remember, he who begs for grace is no longer our foe.

The song, *Viking Code,* embodies some of these rules. Years later, the composer, Crusell, wrote an opera based on the *Fridthjof Saga,* and this is one of the songs he composed for it.

The Viking Code

(From Fridthjof's Saga)

Text by R. O. and B. P. K.

B. CRUSELL (1775 - 1838)
Arr by B. P. K.

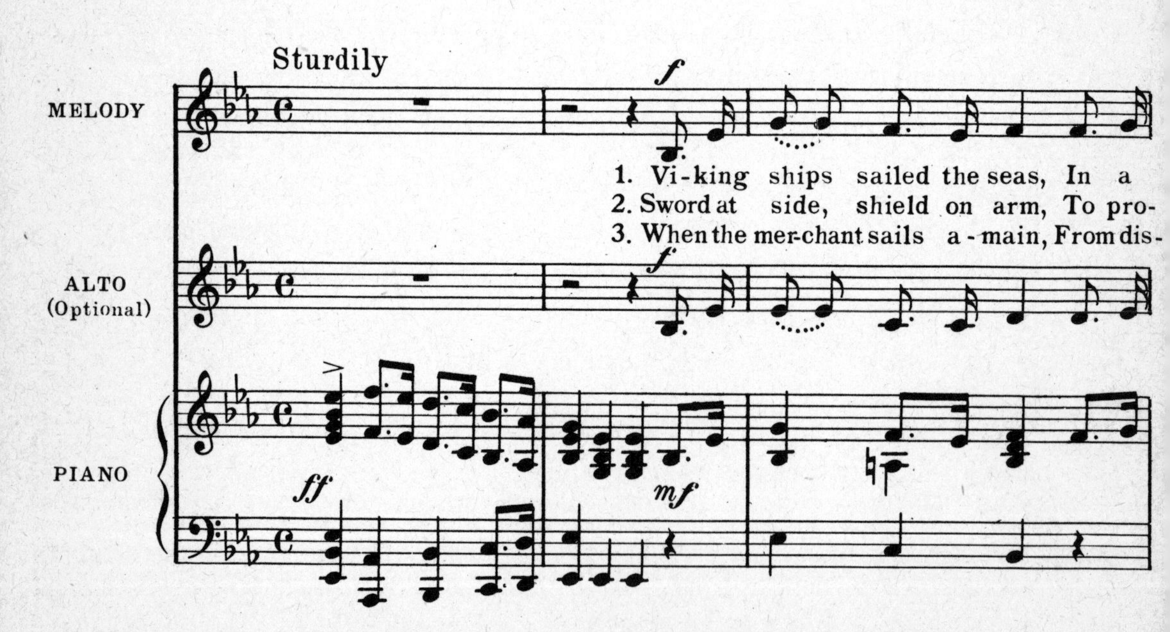

calm, or in breeze, Nev - er fear - ful of weath - er were
tect them from harm, Nev - er sleep in a house was their
turb - ance re - frain, But fair trib - ute he must not with
they; Oh, a vi - king so brave Ne'er a
rule, For with - in ev' - ry door Might be
hold; Mer - chant ships they would save; They were
thought ev - er gave To the storm, or the waves, or the gale.
crouch - ing a foe, This, the code of the brave vi - king crew.
lords of the wave, And as good was their steel, as their gold.

When Fridthjof was tired of roaming the seas, he disguised himself and went to the palace of King Ring. The King secretly recognized him, but because he had taken such a great liking to him, he invited Fridthjof to stay at the castle.

The King, now a very old man, felt that he would soon be taken to Valhalla, the home of the gods and of the heroes who died in battle. Before his death, he bestowed Ingeborg, the Queen, and all his kingdom upon Fridthjof. As in our modern stories, we suppose that the two reunited lovers lived happily ever after.

King Ring's Drapa is another song from the same opera by Crusell. A *drapa* is a funeral song for one who has died. The old ballad upon which this song is based gives us some of the old customs carried on by the Norsemen in regard to burials. King Ring has been buried according to custom, with all his trappings and his favorite horse. His grave is in the side of a hill, and is called in the song, a *throne room*. The old Norsemen believed he finally left this throne room in the hill to go to Valhalla, where he would be welcomed.

King Ring's Drapa

Text adapted from translation by
B. P. K.

B. Crusell (1775 - 1838)
Arr. by B. P. K.

MELODY
mf
hold King_ Ring! Broad sword and gleam-ing shield,
hold King_ Ring! Now all the por-tals wide,
mf
hold King Ring! Broad sword and gleam ing shield,
goal to win; Now all the por-tals wide,
mf
Armed as if to meet the foe, Wild-ly his war-horse is
O - pen in wel - come, He-roes and gods bid him
f
Armed to meet the foe,_ Wild-ly his war-horse is
O - pen in wel - come, He-roes and gods bid him
f
f
paw-ing the ground, Wait-ing his mas-ter's sig-nal to go!
en-ter_ in, Feast-ing and sing-ing, hom-age to Ring.
paw-ing the ground,_ Wait-ing his mas-ter's sig-nal to go!
en-ter_ in,_ Feast-ing and sing-ing, hom-age to Ring.

THE SAGA OF OLAF TRYGVESSON

Olaf Trygvesson has been the idol of the sea-loving people of Norway for centuries. He was born in the year 964 A. D. and died in 1000. He was the son of King Trygve and Queen Astrid who lost their throne when Olaf was a baby. Many years later, because of his strength and fearlessness, Olaf was able to regain his father's throne. When he was still a young man he became a Christian as the result of winning a battle, and after he had reclaimed his father's throne, he forced all Norway to become Christian.

Olaf was never as happy as when he was on the sea. He had three favorite ships in his fleet, the *Little Serpent*, the *Crane*, and the *Long Serpent*. They must have been beautiful boats. They were row-boats of course, and the *Long Serpent* had thirty-four benches, a gilded dragon's head at the bow, and a dragon's tail at the stern.

Olaf was strong, fearless, and light on his feet. He could run across the oars outside of the vessel while his men were rowing the *Serpent*. He could play with three daggers so that one was always in the air, and he always caught the falling one by the handle. He could walk all around the ship's rails, strike and cut with either hand, and throw two spears at once. These are the tales that his own men told about him. It is no wonder that his people have admired him for generations.

The song called *The Ballad of Olaf Trygvesson*, tells the story of one of Olaf's expeditions to a new land to Christianize the people. Edvard Grieg, the most famous of Norway's composers, has given us the music of this fine old song.

The Ballad of Olaf Trygvesson

Text by
B. P. K.

EDVARD GRIEG
Arr. and adapted by B. P. K.

f
1. Lived there a vi-king long a-go, O-laf Tryg-ve-sson was he;
2. And it was O-laf Tryg-ve-sson Land-ed on the shore that day;
Sailed to a king-dom fair and glo-rious, Far o'er the North-ern sea.
Val-iant and kind-ly wise-ly would he rule o'er this land al-way.
mf
f
3
fp
For-est and wa-ter gleam-ing O-laf Tryg-ve-sson felt he sure-ly was dream-ing.
Dark were the waves, fore-bod-ing Yet the val-leys were sweet with wild flow-ers grow-ing.
mf
f
3
3
molto piu lento
p
3. Gai-ly the bells were ring-ing; O-laf Tryg-ve-sson praised God with
p

pp
p
sing - ing,
Praised God with sing - ing.
Solo, with humming chorus the first time only
Second time, Chorus in unison on the melody.
p
Hm
Hm
Hm
p - mf
Here up-on the ground be-fore us,. Let us build a tem-ple
p - mf
cresc. al Fine
Hm
Hm
Hm
cresc. al Fine
glo-rious; Hearts a-glow to tell the sto-ry, Help us Lord to know Thy
cresc. al Fine

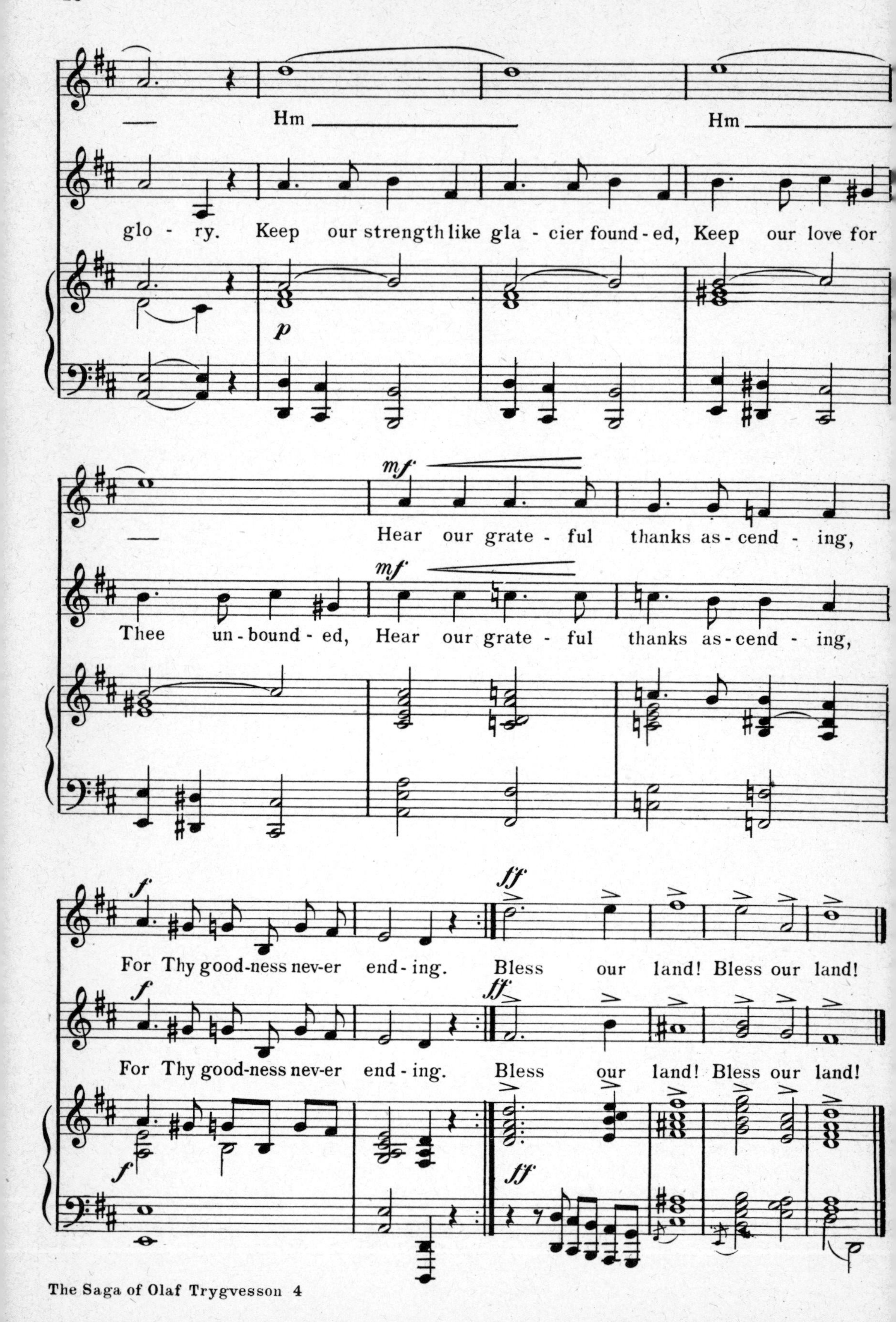
Hm
Hm
glo - ry. Keep our strength like gla - cier found - ed, Keep our love for
p
mf
Hear our grate - ful thanks as - cend - ing,
mf
Thee un - bound - ed, Hear our grate - ful thanks as - cend - ing,
f
For Thy good-ness nev-er end - ing.
ff
Bless our land! Bless our land!
f
For Thy good-ness nev-er end - ing.
ff
Bless our land! Bless our land!
f
ff

NORWEGIAN FOLK SONGS

Not all Norwegian songs are about their heroes, or great events in their history. There are hundreds of beautiful folk songs, and many of them are about everyday people, and the work that they had to do. As you know, the herd girls took their herds of cows and goats into the mountains for the summer pasture. They stayed there all summer spending the time making cheese and butter.

This song is one used by them to call their animals home at night. In this case, each of the cows has its own name. They say the cows never mistake the voice of their own keeper. That is, they never respond to any call except that of their own keeper, nor do they ever get confused by the goat calls which their keeper may use to call her goats home. Here is an example of a goat tune. Notice the names!

Goatkeeper's Song

Notice the little tune which accompanies the Cowkeeper's Song. It is meant for a woodwind instrument like the *tra pipa* (*tray peepa*) which was a little homemade pipe played by these herdgirls while watching their animals in the mountains.

The Cowkeeper's Song

(With instrumental descant)

Translation by
R.O.

Norwegian Folk Song
Arr. by B. P. K.

f
dear one. Come Rau - ty, come Skau - ty, come play - ful Ka - ri, come
f
Kap - pe - lans Ma - ri, come Ron - ke - bu, Jer - sty, Come Ko - lums, Ber - ty, Come
pp
ev - 'ry - one.
dim.
pp

THE OLD WOMAN WITH A CANE

This song has very, very old Norwegian words, and some of its phrases have lost their original meaning through hundreds of years of use. The custom which is still carried on in many Norwegian communities, of telling fortunes with coffee grounds and potato skins, is mentioned here in this song.

The first section of the song is in a typical *springdans* tempo. The second section is typical of the *halling* dance. A *springdans* is a rustic *round dance,* in which two, or groups of two, take part. It is performed with a light, springy step. The *halling* is one of the favorite rustic dances, and is danced only by the young men. Old men or girls would not be able to do this dance at all, because it requires too much strength and athletic ability. The dancer had to kick the beam of the ceiling! Maybe the ceilings were lower in the old Scandinavian homes than they are in our homes today.

The young men who succeeded in kicking the beam were the heroes of the evening. While they were dancing the *halling,* the others were grouped around, watching them. If this song were danced, the girls could sing the second section while the boys performed feats of physical strength, and then when the tune returns to the first section again, all could join in the singing and dancing.

There is another *Springdans* on page 27 and a *Halling* on page 28.

The Old Woman with a Cane

(Kjaerringa med Staven)

Text adapted from translation by
B.P.K.

Norwegian Folk Tune
Arr. by B.P. K.

Fine
She will give you some! Clev - er old___ wo - man!
From the flow - ing brook! Kjaer - riņ - ga med Sta - ven.
Fine
Moderato
DESCANT mf
2. This old wo - man, this old wo - man,
MELODY
f
2. Oh! fa la la la la la la, Fa la la la, la la la,
mf
Al - ways walks with a crook - ed cane. She can jump, and
Fa la la la la la la la la, Fa la la la la la, la,

climb, and scram - ble, You can tell she_ is not lame!
Fa la la la la la la, Fa la la la la la la la la.
MELODY
f
Cof - fee grounds, and thick po - ta - to skins, She'll tell your for - tune in!
DESCANT
mf
Fa la, la la, She will_ tell your_ for - tune in!
mf
D.S. al Fine
rit.
Cof - fee grounds and thick po - ta - to skins! That's when the fun be - gins!
rit.
Fa la, la la, That is_ when the_ fun be - gins!
rit.
D.S. al Fine

Paul on the Hillside

Text by
R.O.

Norse Folk Song
Arr. by B. P. K.

nard — wait - ed, — Read - y to
feared his moth - er's scold - ing, How he —
fox, was a - wait - ing and watch - ing, Read - y to pounce and
fraid that his moth - er would scold him, What should he do? He
car - ry — the hen a - way, "Kluk, kluk, kluk, kluk," The
hat - ed — that wi - ly fox, "Pyt, pyt, pyt, pyt," I'll
car - ry her a - way. "Kluk, kluk, kluk," said the
hat - ed the fox! "Pyt," said Paul, "I shall
hen — on the hill - side, "Kluk, kluk, kluk, kluk, kluk,"
not — be a cow - ard; "Pyt, pyt, pyt, pyt, pyt,"
hen on the hill - side, "Kluk, kluk, kluk," said the
not be a cow - ard; "Pyt," said Paul, "An - y

NORWEGIAN DANCES

We have told you about the two dances, *springdans* and *halling* in connection with the song, *The Old Woman with the Cane*. Here we have another well-known *springdans* from Bergen, Norway.

Notice the left hand accompaniment in the first section. It is always the same chord, and is supposed to represent the drone of the strings (like the bagpipe drone) which were underneath the regular fiddle strings of the Norwegian *Hardanger fiddle*. In other words, this old instrument had two sets of strings. This kind of an accompaniment is often found in Scandinavian music. Grieg used it many times.

Springdans
Norwegian,
from Bergen
Vivace
PIANO
mf–f
Fine
p–f
1
2
D.C. al Fine

Halling

EDVARD GRIEG

Edvard Grieg was born in 1843, in Bergen, Norway. His mother was his first music teacher, and she gave him piano lessons when he was a very small boy. At a very early age he was writing his own music.

At first the people did not care about Grieg's music. In fact, even after he was married he had a hard time getting along, and he had to take much of his time away from his composing in order to give piano lessons. Grieg was a very fine pianist, and his wife had a beautiful voice, so they were able to spend many hours together working in music.

After Grieg was twenty-six years old, he received an income each year from the government, in order that he might spend all his time composing. By this time, of course, the Norwegian people had come to love Grieg's music, perhaps because so much of it was based on their own songs and beloved tunes.

Grieg called his home "Troldhaugen," which means, "Hill of the Trolls." No matter how far away he travelled, or how many honors he received, he was always happy to get back to Troldhaugen.

When Grieg died at the age of sixty-four, in 1907, he was famous all over Europe, and greatly beloved by all the people in his own land. When he was buried, it is said that thirty thousand people came from his beloved Bergen to pay their last respects to the great composer. All the boats in the harbor flew flags at half mast, and all the houses in Bergen hoisted the national colors as a sign of mourning.

EVENING SONG FOR BLAKKEN

This is one of the loveliest songs which Grieg wrote for children. *Blakken* is the name of the little horse. The word *Fola* doesn't mean anything in particular. In English it might stand for "there now" or "come, come."

pp
Fo - la, Blak - ken, Fo - la, fo - la, Blak - ken.
Fo - la, Blak - ken, Fo - la, fo - la, Blak - ken.
fo - la, fo - la, Blak - ken.
see to that, dear Blak - ken.
pp
p
mf MELODY
O'er the high - way, O - ver moun-tains all the way,
Sweet dreams Blak - ken, For to - mor - row we shall play,
mf
p
O'er the rock - y high - way, O - ver moun-tains all the way,
Pleas-ant dreams my Blak - ken, For to - mor - row we shall play,
You have earned your food to - day, Our dear, old, gen - tle Blak - ken.
Sun - day is your hol - i - day, There'll be no work for Blak - ken.
You have earned your food to - day, Our dear, old, gen - tle Blak - ken.
Sun - day is your hol - i - day, There'll be no work for Blak - ken.

pp
a tempo molto tranquillo
p MELODY
Dear, gen - tle Blak - ken.
No work for Blak - ken.
3. Dream on that, my Blak - ken,
pp
Slum - ber,
pp
p
rit. poco a poco al fine
pp
Naught to do but eat and rest, Do the things you like the best, And
p
On - ly eat and rest, Slum - ber,
rit. poco a poco al fine
now, good night, my Blak - ken.
good night, Blak - ken.
pp

DANISH MUSIC

Danish Ballads

Of all the Scandinavian countries, Denmark has done the most to preserve her old ballads so that they may be learned and enjoyed by her people today.

As in the case of those of the other Scandinavian countries, these ballads are often based on some historical person or event, although many times the actual details of the various stanzas have been worked on by the imagination.

Marsk Stig lived in Denmark centuries ago. There are many ballads about him and his lovely wife. The ballad here is about his daughters, and their fate after the death of Marsk Stig and his wife.

Like most ballads, this one has a refrain which ends each stanza. It preserves the tragic mood, even though some of the stanzas begin quite gaily.

Another reason for having a refrain at the end of a ballad was that it gave the audience a chance to take part in the performance. The ballad was begun by a leader, called the "fore-singer," and while the entire group was adding the refrain, he had time to think ahead and have the next part of his story ready when it came his turn to continue.

As we might expect, through hundreds of years of usage, the refrains of many ballads have become confused, and have lost all their original meaning. To us they sound like nonsense. This is especially true of some of the dance-songs. This is not difficult to understand when we remember our own experiences in trying to sing words and dance vigorously at the same time.

The Three Rascals, on page 36 is an example of a song with a nonsense refrain.

The ballad, *Marsk Stig's Daughters,* is fun to recite while people representing the characters dramatize the story. It may be either sung or recited while it is being dramatized.

Marsk Stig's Daughters

Text by B.P.K.

Danish Folk Ballad
Arr by B.P.K.

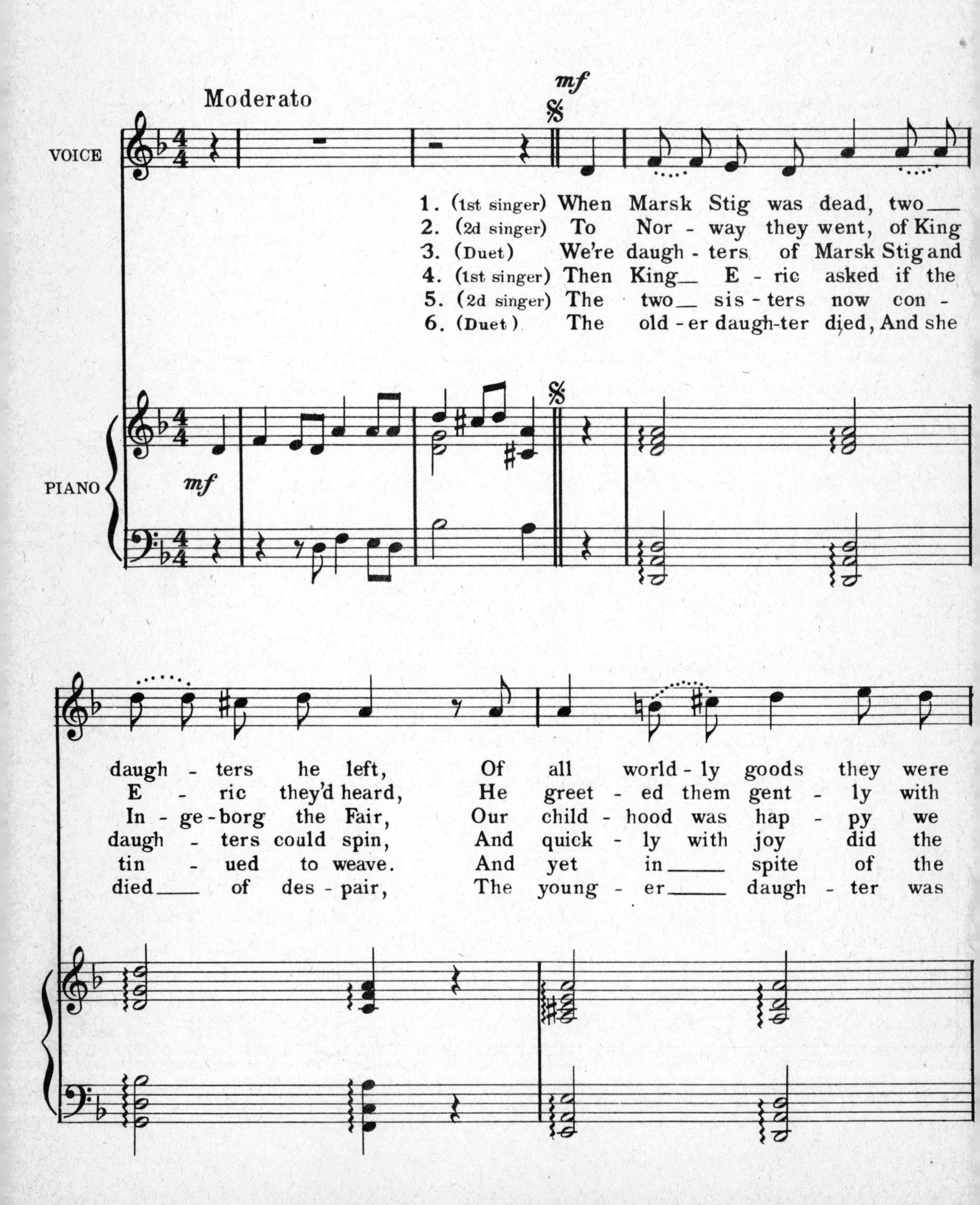

tru - ly be-reft; To leave their home they bit - ter - ly wept,
com-fort - ing words; The maid - ens' hearts at once he stirred;
knew not a care; A - las! Cru-el fate! We can - not bear;
sis - ters be - gin. So pleased was the King, he in-vit-ed them in,
gifts they'd re-ceive, The eld - est one con - tin - ued to grieve,
love - ly and fair. The King's son asked her his life to share,
Refrain (Chorus)
D.S.
A - lone in the wide world to wan - der.
A - lone in the wide world to wan - der.
A - lone in the wide world to wan - der.
No more in the wide world to wan - der.
A - lone in the wide world she'd wan - dered.
No more in the wide world she'll wan - der.
Fine
p
D.S.

The Three Rascals

This is an example of an entirely different kind of ballad. Remember these ballads were meant to be dramatized, danced, and sung. It is easy to dance to the refrain in this song, especially when the chorus is in a large circle.

lus - di - lay.
mf Solo (or small group)
They were off to the mill for to
lus - tu - di - lay. Then___ one slung the sack on the
The___ sack start - ed creep - ing and
(Joker) "Pret - ty maid - en please say; Will you
mf
see the mil - ler? Nay! Twas his daugh - ter they say!
oth - er fel - low's back; Cour - age they did not lack!
mov - ing 'round the room, Not a light from the moon!
mar - ry me, I pray? Ans - wer 'Yea' or___ 'Nay'. The
Chorus
Pret - ty maid,___ Can't you see? Can't you see?
"Mil - ler, say,___ Grind our corn, Grind to - day?"
(Girls) "Fa - ther, dear,___ Do I hear? Do I hear?"
mil - ler came,___ Scratched his head, Then he said,
Pret - ty maid, Can___ you not see?
"Mil - ler, say, Grind our corn to - day?"
(She) "Fa - ther, dear, What___ do I hear?"
mil - ler came, Scratched his head and said,

Refrain (Chorus)
Tin, tan, lus - di - lay! Solo
Oh
Tin - glu - ti, tan - glu - ti, lus - tu - di - lay! (Miller) "Oh,
(She) For
(Miller) "The
(or small group)
you can't de - pend, You sure - ly will a -
leave it at the door, for I can do no
sure ly the cat is chas - ing the
rat has gone, but this fun - ny
1,2,3
4
gree, On these ras - cals three!
more, But to - mor - row I may!"
rat, And it's ver - y near!"
cat left his big boots on!"

Rosalil

Text adapted from translation by
B. P. K.

Danish Folk Song
Arr. by B.P.K.

* Sing the Descant on stanzas 1,3 and 4 only. Sing it on all the Refrains however.

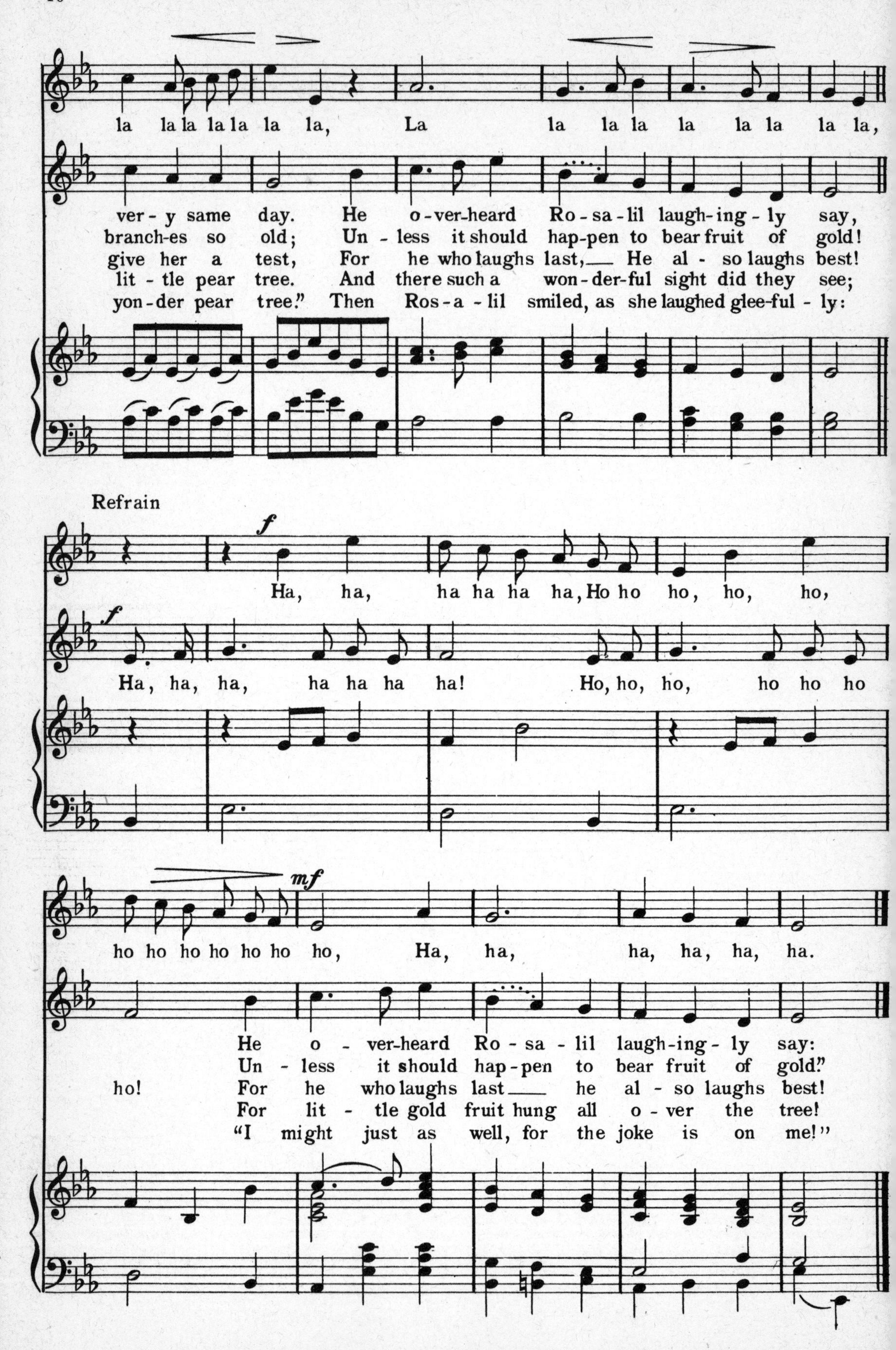
la la la la la la la, La la la la la la la la la,
ver - y same day. He o - ver - heard Ro - sa - lil laugh - ing - ly say,
branch - es so old; Un - less it should hap - pen to bear fruit of gold!
give her a test, For he who laughs last, He al - so laughs best!
lit - tle pear tree. And there such a won - der - ful sight did they see;
yon - der pear tree." Then Ros - a - lil smiled, as she laughed glee - ful - ly:
Refrain
f
Ha, ha, ha ha ha ha, Ho ho ho, ho, ho,
f
Ha, ha, ha, ha ha ha ha! Ho, ho, ho, ho ho ho
mf
ho ho ho ho ho ho ho, Ha, ha, ha, ha, ha, ha.
He o - ver - heard Ro - sa - lil laugh - ing - ly say:
Un - less it should hap - pen to bear fruit of gold."
ho! For he who laughs last he al - so laughs best!
For lit - tle gold fruit hung all o - ver the tree!
"I might just as well, for the joke is on me!"

HANS CHRISTIAN ANDERSON

Most of us remember *Hans Christian Anderson* as the author of many delightful fairy tales. Some of these stories have been set to music, such as *The Princess and the Swineherd*. Scandinavian composers have set some of his verses to music, also. Here we have two songs, the verses of which were originally written by Hans Christian Anderson.

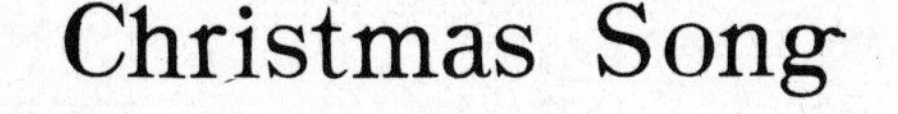

lul - - la - by,
Lul - la - by, lul - a - by, lul - la - by,
heav'n - ly crown up - on His head. A star for light in
Child is born in Beth - le - hem". Now those who would the
lul - a - by
Lul - lay, lul - la - by,
dark - ness deep, An ox to kiss His ti - ny feet, His
Christ - child find, And leave all grief and care be - hind, Must
cresc. (second stanza)
p-f
Lul - lay, lul - la - by, Hal - le - lu - jah!
cresc. (second stanza)
p-f
Moth - er's love to guard His sleep, Hal - le - lu - jah!
child - ren be in heart and mind, Hal - le - lu - jah!
cresc. (2nd time)
p-f

Cuckoo, Fallera!

From the poem by
HANS CHRISTIAN ANDERSON
Adapted by B.P.K.

Danish Folk Song
Arr by B.P.K.

* A solo voice may sing the "Cuckoos."

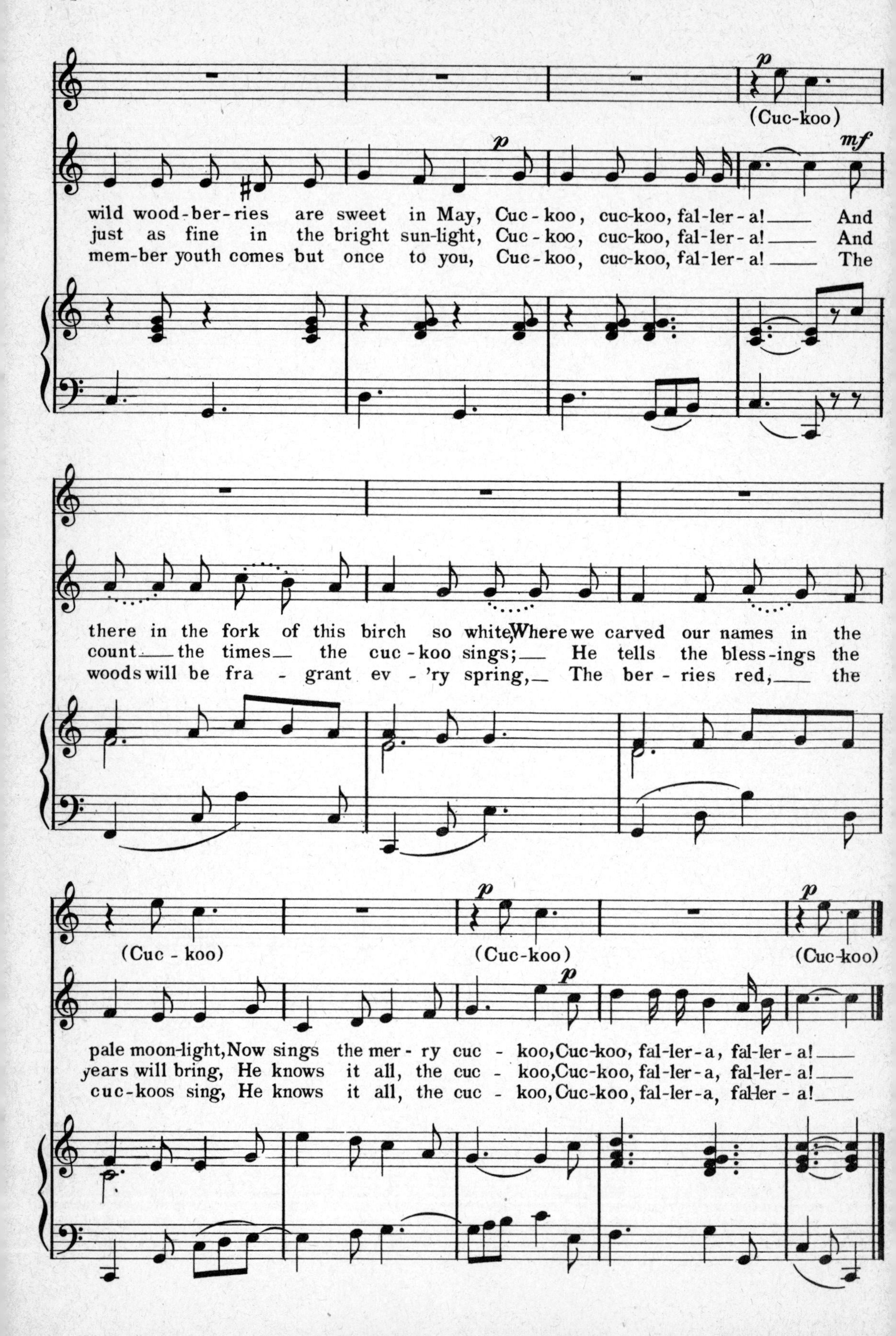
(Cuc-koo)
wild wood-ber-ries are sweet in May, Cuc-koo, cuc-koo, fal-ler-a! And
just as fine in the bright sun-light, Cuc-koo, cuc-koo, fal-ler-a! And
mem-ber youth comes but once to you, Cuc-koo, cuc-koo, fal-ler-a! The
there in the fork of this birch so white, Where we carved our names in the
count the times the cuc-koo sings; He tells the bless-ings the
woods will be fra-grant ev-'ry spring, The ber-ries red, the
(Cuc-koo)
(Cuc-koo)
(Cuc-koo)
pale moon-light, Now sings the mer-ry cuc-koo, Cuc-koo, fal-ler-a, fal-ler-a!
years will bring, He knows it all, the cuc-koo, Cuc-koo, fal-ler-a, fal-ler-a!
cuc-koos sing, He knows it all, the cuc-koo, Cuc-koo, fal-ler-a, fal-ler-a!

HOLGER DANSKE (HOLGER, THE DANE)

This is the name given to a great Danish hero. It means Holger, the Dane. He may have lived, or he may be only a legend in the hearts of his people.

At any rate, Holger the Dane is supposed to sit in the dungeon of the Kronberg Castle, at the great table in the old dining hall. Here he has slept through the ages, and his beard has grown down to the table. The tale goes that in Denmark's hour of greatest need he will awake, and, as in days of old, again lead her to victory!

Niels Gade was the greatest Danish composer of the nineteenth century.

Holger the Dane

(His Greeting to the Fatherland)

(Holger Danske)

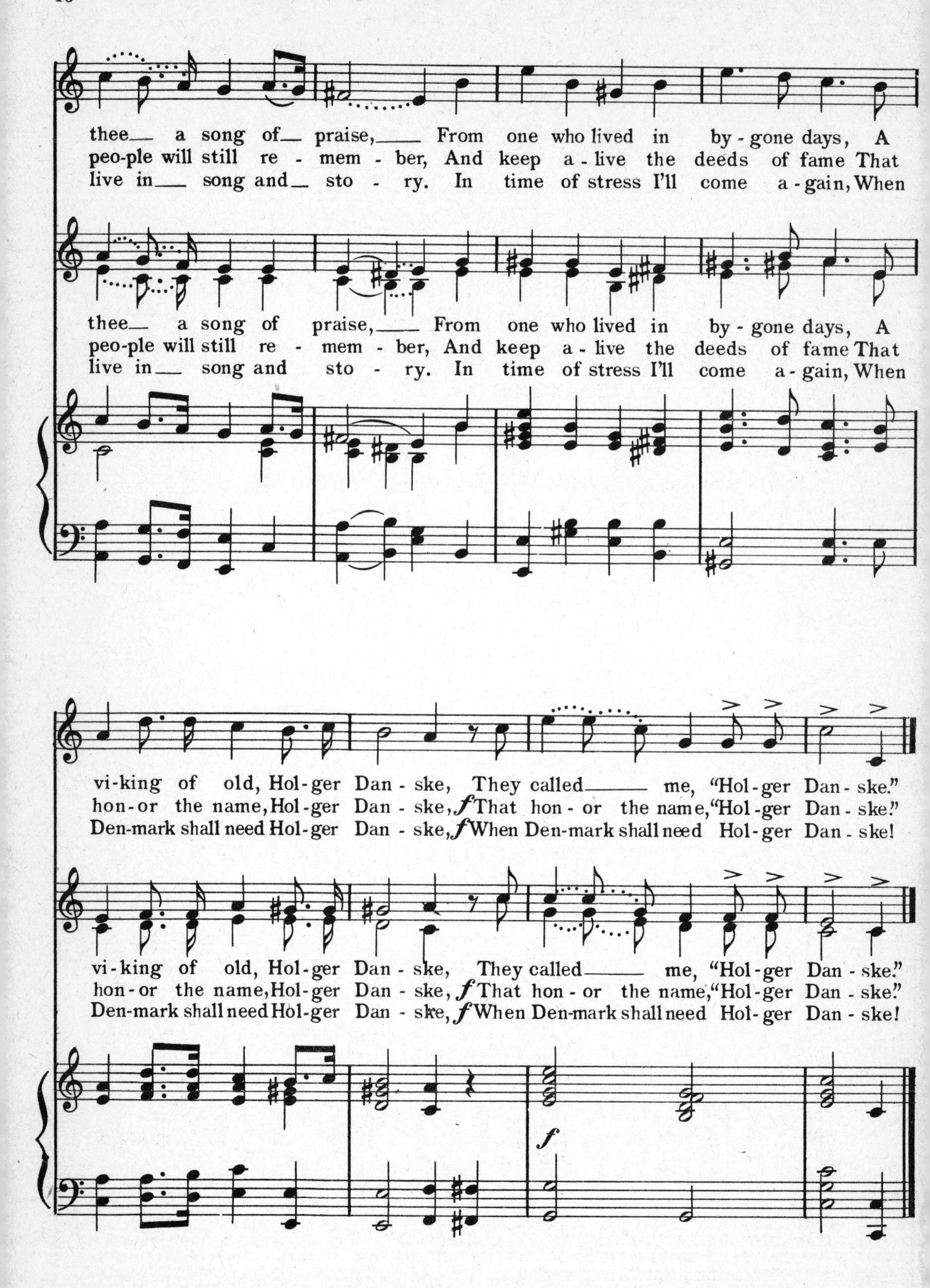
thee— a song of— praise,— From one who lived in by - gone days, A
peo-ple will still re - mem - ber, And keep a - live the deeds of fame That
live in— song and— sto - ry. In time of stress I'll come a - gain, When
thee— a song of praise,— From one who lived in by - gone days, A
peo-ple will still re - mem - ber, And keep a - live the deeds of fame That
live in— song and sto - ry. In time of stress I'll come a - gain, When
vi-king of old, Hol-ger Dan - ske, They called— me, "Hol-ger Dan - ske."
hon-or the name, Hol-ger Dan - ske, f That hon - or the name, "Hol-ger Dan - ske."
Den-mark shall need Hol-ger Dan - ske, f When Den-mark shall need Hol-ger Dan - ske!
vi-king of old, Hol-ger Dan - ske, They called— me, "Hol-ger Dan - ske."
hon-or the name, Hol-ger Dan - ske, f That hon - or the name, "Hol-ger Dan - ske."
Den-mark shall need Hol-ger Dan - ske, f When Den-mark shall need Hol-ger Dan - ske!
f

Little Ola, the Sandman

Ole Lukøje

This song is sung in Sweden as well as in Denmark. It really is of Danish origin. It is sometimes called *Ola Lukoje,* which, if it were translated literally would mean *Ola Closed-eye,* or *Ola Shut-eye.* In our country we would probably call him the Sandman, although we picture him with a big bag over his back, rather than with an umbrella, as the Danish people usually think of him.

mf MELODY
Ah This lit-tle Sand-man, they call him
He'll tell them sto-ries of man-y
p DESCANT
quaint-ed in all the towns.
dream-ers with peace-ful sleep.
Ah
p DESCANT
O-la, Each eve-ning he makes his rounds.
won-ders, 'Til morn-ing his watch he'll keep.
mf MELODY
And ev-'ry eve-ning he makes his rounds.
Un-til the morn-ing his watch he'll keep.
13620